THE DEAD DETECTIVE

IN

DEAD AND UNBURIED

THE DEAD DETECTIVE

IN

DEAD AND UNBURIED

by Felix Bogarte™

Published 2003 by Books Noir Ltd, Glasgow

Text written by Joan Love and Mhairi MacDiarmid,
based on a story by Mhairi MacDiarmid

A CIP catalogue for this book is available from the British Library

ISBN 1-904684-00-9

Printed and bound in the EU

www.booksnoir.com

www.deaddetective.com

info@deaddetective.com

CONTENTS

CHAPTER ONE

LOS ANGELES, 1953

HANK pushed his way to the front of the crowd of onlookers and headed for the apartment block.

"Captain Hank Kane," he snarled at a rookie cop. The cop glanced at Hank's ID and let him into the crime scene.

Hank made his way up to the penthouse apartment. Forensics were already there, doing what Forensics do. Hank merely wanted to be allowed to do what *he* had to do before he went off duty for the night.

The call had come in over an hour ago, when Hank had just sat down to have a well-earned cup of coffee and a doughnut. He'd had a hell of a long day, most of it spent stuck behind his desk catching up on the paperwork he hated having to do. He should have been glad to get out of the precinct for a while but sitting behind his desk all day had made him even grouchier than ever. All he wanted to do now was to go home.

Hank recognised one of the other detectives. "Hey, Al, howya doin?" he asked. The detective was crouched down on the floor of the apartment looking as if he had been giving the corpse its last rites but he straightened up when he saw Hank.

"Doin' okay, Hank," he replied as he offered his outstretched hand. Hank flinched. Al had a rather unfortunate skin condition and spent most of his time scratching. His sweaty palms didn't seem very appealing so Hank just shook Al's fingers very gingerly.

Al took a small notebook from his pocket and flicked open a page. "Name's Charlie McCall," he said, indicating the body. "Dead when we got here. Shot right through the heart, one bullet. Good shot, whoever shot him."

Hank nodded. He knew McCall. He bent to look more closely at the body spread-eagled on the floor before them. McCall had fallen awkwardly, bashing his head against the edge of a glass coffee table. Hank wondered who lived here. It certainly wasn't Charlie McCall's pad.

"Think it's some sort of gangster thing?" asked Al as he scratched his jaw and looked at Hank.

"Could be," said Hank. He smirked. "Either that or he had a row with his girl."

Al laughed. Charlie McCall's girl was a real tough cookie. The two were well known for their fiery arguments. Some even said that was what kept them together. But she wouldn't have shot him. Would she?

"Somehow I don't think this little fiasco was a domestic," said Hank, rubbing the black stubble which adorned his chin.

A police officer appeared at the door. He'd been questioning the neighbours.

"Found anything yet?" Hank asked him.

The officer scratched his head with his pencil. "Nothing much to report so far. No-one seems to have heard anything…which would suggest a silencer had been used on the gun."

"No kiddin', Sherlock…" Hank drawled sarcastically. "Keep that up kid and you'll have a job like mine someday. Nothing else?"

"The old lady two doors down says she saw the deceased, though he wasn't deceased then, obviously…"

Hank sighed. It was going to be a long night.

"He arrived just after eight this evening. She remembers the time because *The Jack Benny Show* had just started and she always listens to him. Her husband died about seven years ago, and she says they always used to listen to it together. Only now he's gone…"

"Kid, if I wanted to know about *Jack Benny* I'd have stayed at home and listened to him. Just get to the point!"

"Yes, sir, sorry sir. Well, em, there isn't that much to tell really. The old lady says she saw him arrive, alone, then she went off to watch television. A couple of hours later she heard a car pull up and went to look out her window."

"Did she see anything?" asked Hank, becoming more interested.

"It was us, sir. The police car arriving."

Hank looked at the young cop in disbelief. "Ever thought of some other line of work, son?"

Al had started scratching again. Hank decided it was time to leave.

"Let me know if Forensics come up with anything," he said, as he made his way out the door, "though I've got a pretty good idea who did this."

Al looked up at Hank. The look on his face was one of pure awe.

Hank climbed into his car, started up the engine and headed for home. Tomorrow would be time enough to pay a visit to his old friend, Johnny Malcolm.

CHAPTER TWO

GUT INSTINCT

"SUNNY side up, twice. And some black coffee," said Hank, almost barking his order at the waitress.

"The word 'please' obviously ain't in your vocabulary," she said. She finished writing his order in her pad and made her way to the rear of the diner.

Hank started to read his newspaper and ignored her. He wasn't in the mood for niceties this morning. He'd slept very badly last night, got up this morning and discovered he had no milk, no bread, and no coffee. He really must employ someone to clean up for him, and pay the odd visit to the supermarket. Ever since he'd split from his long-time girlfriend about a year ago, his eating habits had steadily got worse.

His weekly shopping consisted of a few chocolate bars and some TV dinners. He sighed inwardly. Hazel had been lovely, a really nice girl, but she just hadn't been able to put up with the long hours cops put in.

Okay, he'd admit grudgingly, he could have cut

the hours a bit and gotten home earlier on a few occasions. But what these broads didn't seem to understand was that being a cop was his life; the guys all had the same things in common and he liked the atmosphere of the precinct. Plus, the streets wouldn't stay safe by themselves.

He mopped up the last of his eggs, drained the coffee from his cup, picked up his newspaper and left. The waitress watched as he shut the door behind him and then went over to clear his table.

She picked up the quarter he'd left on his side plate. "Last of the big spenders," she thought wryly as she slipped the money into her apron pocket. "Shame, too, he was kinda cute."

Hank got out of his car and put on his sunglasses to shield his eyes from the sun. He was outside one of the large car lots that Johnny Malcolm owned, though he was unsure whether the man himself was inside or not. He decided to go in.

The girl on reception was picking at her nail varnish. Some of her nails were bright red, others were chipped and broken. She had perspiration on her upper lip. The fan was broken again, on one of the hottest days of the year. She pulled at the neck of her blue, wool jacket. Johnny insisted that all his staff had to wear uniforms but he was too mean to buy them lighter suits for the summer months. The girl switched her attention from her nails to a chocolate bar. She took a large bite and glanced up at Hank.

"Morning, sir," she mumbled, chocolate crumbs now adorning her sweating top lip. "What can I do for you?"

"Mr Malcolm in?" Hank asked.

"You got an appointment, sir?"

"Nope. But you tell him Hank Kane's here. He'll see me."

Hank took a seat. The girl pressed a key on her switchboard and got connected to Mr Malcolm's office.

"Rosie? It's Freda on reception. I got a Mr Hank Kane to see Mr Malcolm. No, he doesn't have an appointment. Maybe you could check for me if Mr Malcolm would like to see him or not? You will? Okay, you can let me know."

She replaced the handset on the switchboard and took another large bite from the chocolate bar.

Hank flicked through the out-of-date magazines on the coffee table in front of him. Why did no-one ever put up-to-date magazines in their offices? Who wanted to know what were the best sauces for a turkey when it was the middle of June? Come to think of it, who would want to know that anyway?

The girl on reception had finished the bar of chocolate and had started on a piece of chewing gum. Hank hoped Johnny would hurry up. He was bored.

The door next to the reception was pushed open and a tall, good-looking blonde woman held it open.

"Mr Kane?" she inquired, raising an eyebrow.

Hank got up. "That's me," he replied smiling, boredom fast disappearing.

"Mr Malcolm will see you now, if you'd like to come with me."

"With pleasure," said Hank, as he followed her down a narrow hallway. She stopped outside a room bearing a gold sign with the words: "J Malcolm, Managing Director" inscribed on it. She pushed it open and motioned for Hank to go in.

Johnny's huge figure was barely discernible in the smoke-filled room. He must have been on his tenth cigar of the morning. "And to think I was worried about *my* health," thought Hank.

Waving his hand in front of his face, Hank

found a chair and sat down. "Can't you at least open a window in here, Johnny?"

"Good morning to you, too," said Johnny in his high-pitched voice.

It never ceased to amaze Hank how a man of Johnny Malcolm's huge size could have such a silly little voice. Johnny weighed in at about two hundred pounds but held the belief that wearing suits which were a shade too small for him made him look thinner. He refused to admit to being a larger size than he actually was.

He had lost most of his hair and spent his time trying to comb what was left of it into some sort of style on top of his head. All in all, he was a very large man with a very small brain.

The only reason he had a string of car lots across the state was because his father had been an incredibly astute businessman. Unfortunately, his life had been cut prematurely short but Johnny had inherited his empire. He was lucky that a lot of his father's employees remained loyal to the memory of Mr Malcolm senior, and so the business still did reasonably well.

Hank looked at Johnny carefully. "Where were you yesterday between the hours of three and five pm?" asked Hank.

"Ah, no small talk this morning at all?" grinned Johnny. "And I was good enough to see you without an appointment." He stopped smiling and leant forward on his desk.

"Why do you want to know?" he asked.

"The Police Department are curious," replied Hank. "Charlie McCall was found shot dead yesterday and we all know you and he weren't exactly good friends."

Johnny extinguished his cigar. "Doesn't make me a killer. Look around you, Hank. Look at my kingdom. McCall is small fry. He means nothing to me. What makes you think I'd have anything to do with taking him out?"

"Oh just the fact that he was heavily involved in stashing stolen guns, crimes committed against the Federal Reserve, that sort of thing. Not exactly 'small fry', Johnny. Also the fact that he was about to take over your business."

Johnny reached into his drawer and Hank found himself becoming tense. Johnny pulled out his cigar clipper.

"What's the matter, Hank? You feelin' a bit nervous? Told you I ain't no killer."

Hank relaxed back into his chair. What was the matter with him? He must be losing it.

Johnny lit the cigar and exhaled. A long slow stream of smoke cut through the heavy cloud already filling the room.

"I was here, working. Check with Rosie. I had nothing to do with McCall's murder. That's not my bag. I'm clean, Hank. Check my diary if you like."

Hank smiled wryly. "Yeah, like your diary entry for the day would include 'kill Charlie'. I think I know better, Johnny. I'm going to see Forensics when I leave here, and you can bet your sweet bottom dollar they're going to find something which will prove your involvement."

"That's your speciality, isn't it Hank? Pinning things on people. Lying about evidence, putting people away when you're not even sure whether they're guilty or not?"

Hank leapt from his chair and grabbed Malcolm's collar. The huge man almost choked, falling backwards in his seat at the unexpected attack. "Don't you ever…" hissed Hank through gritted teeth. "I have never, ever, get me, NEVER put anyone away who wasn't guilty and don't you forget it." Malcolm's eyes bulged in their sockets and sweat ran from his brow.

Hank stared at him for a few seconds longer,

then slowly let go of his collar. "You would do well to remember that *I'm* the accuser here." He almost spat out the words as he turned to leave. "And I have the LAPD on my side, the biggest gang in town."

He slammed the door as he left, almost colliding with Rosie, who straightened up and tried not to look as though she'd been listening at the door.

"Maybe you'd better give your boss some air… he looks a bit hot under the collar," he advised, as he straightened his tie and left the building.

He climbed into his car and searched in his pocket for a cigarette. None. He reached over to check the glove compartment and then remembered. He'd given them up almost a year ago. Johnny Malcolm's accusation had been almost enough to break his carefully controlled temper. Okay, so he had a reputation for "helping evidence along" on some cases. So what? He knew when someone was guilty. He relied heavily on his gut instinct and he was darn sure he wasn't going to sit back and watch criminals go free just because of some stupid loophole in the law.

No sir, Hank Kane wasn't in the habit of letting go when there was a chance of a conviction.

Besides, bad guys don't deserve to share the streets with decent folks. And his gut was telling him that Johnny Malcolm was guilty. It was also telling him that the two eggs he'd had that morning had been a mistake. He turned the key in the ignition and drove off.

CHAPTER THREE

"SURE I CAN PROVE IT"

"HEY, Jack, found anything yet?" Hank asked as he entered the Forensic's laboratory.

Jack looked up from the evidence he had been examining. "Nope, nothing yet, Hank." He noticed Hank looking at some bagged fibres. "Be careful would you, don't touch anything you're not supposed to."

"Don't worry," laughed Hank, "I know the drill by now."

"That's what worries me," smiled Jack, without looking up. He too knew the drill; the unspoken drill that meant he rarely looked up when Hank was in the room. Unless Hank asked him to.

He and Jack had been friends ever since they played together on the precinct's baseball team. They hadn't been any good but somehow their sense of camaraderie had gotten stronger each time they were beaten. That and the fact that Jack was so darn smart at his job. Hank respected anyone who could convict a murderer from a spot of blood left on a carpet.

Hank idly fingered a couple of the bagged fibres. Jack looked up.

"Relax," Hank raised his hands in defence. "I'm not destroying valuable evidence; just curious as to what you've got in there."

"Fibres from McCall's shirt, carpet fibres and some hairs which may or may not be Gloria's. If they're hers, it's kinda inconclusive. I mean why wouldn't the guy have some of his girlfriend's hairs on his clothes?"

Hank nodded. "Okay, Jack, I'm gonna leave you to it. Got a few more people I need to see today. Let me know when you come up with something, won't you?"

Jack nodded in return and put his eye back to the microscope. He'd let Hank know, but for now he and his team had a lot of work to do.

Hank walked the few blocks back to his own office. He sat down on his chair and picked up some papers he'd been working on the day before. He hummed as he did so. Jessica, one of the rookies in the precinct smiled as she walked past. "You look happy Hank. Havin' a good day?" she asked.

Hank waved her into his office. "Sit down, Jess. Yeah, having a great day as it happens. Just been over to see Johnny Malcolm this morning. Know him?"

"Malcolm? Malcolm?" she said aloud. "Oh yeah, I got it. Huge guy, always perspires heavily, inherited his father's businesses, finger in every pie."

"That's the one," Hank smiled. "Only now he's turned his hand to other things."

"Like what?"

"Like his business was under threat from a man called Charlie McCall. McCall's a bright young guy who knew more about Malcolm's business than Malcolm did himself. He'd a great team working with him and from what I hear they were just about ready to take over. Only now their plans have suffered a setback."

"Oh?" Jessica looked interested. "What happened?"

"McCall was shot dead. Yesterday. And I think I know just who did it."

"You think Johnny Malcolm did it?"

"I sure do."

"But he's never been involved in that sort of thing before. Fraud, sure, stolen weapons, grand theft, but not murder."

Jessica looked at Hank quizzically.

"Trust me on this one, Jess. He did it. Sure as eggs is eggs. He's our man."

"Can you prove it?"

Hank smiled slowly and turned to look out of his window. It was lunchtime and people were leaving the stores clutching coffees, Cokes and cakes. They were trying frantically to find a place on one of the impossibly crowded benches which lined the street.

"Sure I can prove it, honey. Just give me a bit of time."

It was Thursday, three days after the murder and Jack still hadn't called. Hank paced up and down his office checking his watch impatiently. He'd wait till nine am then take a walk up to Forensics. He didn't want to bother his friend but he was impatient to get on with this case. He hated people like Johnny Malcolm committing crimes and getting away with it. In his book, that sort of thing just shouldn't be allowed to happen.

At one minute to nine his phone rang.

"Kane," he said, into the mouthpiece.

"Hank, it's Jack here. Want to take a walk up

here when you've got a minute? Got something to show you."

Hank replaced the receiver with a smile. Good old Jack. Always came up with the goods.

CHAPTER FOUR

GUILTY!

HANK looked with barely concealed disgust at the expanding rings of perspiration under Johnny Malcolm's armpits. Beads of sweat ran from his brow and dripped onto the collar of his shirt. He mopped at his face with a hanky and it was evident to all in the courtroom that his hands shook as he did so. Time was moving on and Hank wanted a verdict.

The jury had just filed back into the courtroom. The trial had gone quite well, Hank thought, considering Johnny Malcolm had never been accused of such a serious crime as murder before.

However, just in case there had been any doubt over his guilt, Forensics had found that the piece of thread discovered under Charlie McCall's fingernails had been a perfect match for Malcolm's suit collar. That had sealed it.

Hank sat back and waited for the verdict.

"Has the Jury found a verdict?"

"We have, your Honour," replied the spokesman.

The verdict was read aloud.

"Guilty."

Malcolm almost collapsed. Two policemen joined him in the witness stand and stood on either side, ready to escort him to his cell. Almost as though in a nightmare, he was aware of the judge sentencing him... "not less a period of twenty-five years, for first degree murder".

Malcolm looked over at Hank as he was led away, his knees almost buckling beneath him.

"You liar, Kane, you planted that evidence. I'll get you for this. You framed me, set me up, just like you've set up every guy before me. You're not good enough to convict on hard evidence, you have to plant it. I'll get you…"

"Take him down," boomed the judge.

Hank got up and walked slowly from the courtroom with Johnny Malcolm's accusing words ringing in his ears.

"Framed… set up… not good enough."

"Yeah, right," muttered Hank as he got up to leave the court room. "Remind me to buy you a brain next time I'm at the store," he smirked in Malcolm's direction as he left.

He pushed open the heavy outer doors of the court and made his way into the sunshine. Darn this humidity. There was no more air out here than there had been in the court. He took off his jacket and started to descend the large stone steps which led down to the street.

He walked towards a diner, two blocks down, planning to buy a late breakfast. He swung his jacket over his shoulder and smiled to himself as he walked down the streets. Streets that now had one less piece of garbage to deal with.

The sound of a police siren interrupted his train of thought. He could see immediately what was happening. Two guys had been disturbed in the process of robbing the store just across the street from where Hank now stood.

One was running down the street. The other was determined to grab as much cash as he possibly could. Hank could see him wielding his gun in the terrified storekeeper's face, whilst cramming notes from the till into a bag. The police car swung into the street and two cops jumped out. One ran after the escaping robber, the second headed for the store.

Hank crossed the road quickly, and joined the first police officer in the chase. The second officer entered the store and drew his gun. He signalled to the storekeeper to go into the back and shouted to the robber to throw down his gun. The robber was sweating profusely, partly due to the heat of the afternoon, but mostly due to the adrenaline and fear pumping through his veins. His hand shook as he pointed his gun at the cop.

"Get outta my way," he shouted. "Ain't no-one gonna take me in! You put *your* gun down. Stay where you are and I won't hurt no-one. I'm leavin' the store now. You put down your gun!"

He looked wildly around the store. Where had Rick, his brother, gone? What had happened to him? They had been planning this robbery for weeks and now just when they were about to pull it off, they had taken their eyes off the store-keeper for just a minute too long, giving the guy enough time to raise the alarm.

He found himself actually thinking of using the gun – the gun he had brought with him to merely scare people. He had to get out of here, and fast, before he found himself on a murder charge.

The cop did as he was told and put his weapon down. He had seen the look on the robber's face and had been in the force long enough to know when someone was desperate. And this guy was desperate enough to shoot if approached the wrong way. The cop put his hands in the air and let the robber leave the store. He wouldn't get far.

A few blocks down, Hank was in hot pursuit of Rick. The first cop had taken a wrong turn, leaving Hank to finish the chase. He wished he were ten years younger; his breathing was becoming more and more laboured as he continued with the chase. However the gap was closing and he had Rick in his sights.

He was unaware, however, that just behind him, Rick's brother, Marco, was closing in, gun still in hand. When Marco saw Hank chasing his brother, real panic had set in. Hank was in his way, in every sense. He had to take action.

Hank couldn't quite figure out why he suddenly wasn't capable of running any more. He found himself falling to the ground and knew something had gone terribly wrong. He could feel a searing hot pain in his back and just before he lost consciousness he realised what had happened. For the first time, in all his years working as a cop, he'd been shot.

CHAPTER FIVE

THE COURT OF GHOULS

HANK woke up slowly in a strangely sterile room that was bathed completely in an eerie white light. His mouth was bone dry and he badly needed a drink of water.

He began to remember. He'd been shot. Must have been one of the punks who had been robbing the store. All those years on the force and some young punk manages to get off a bullet in the right direction. He would have shaken his head in disbelief but it was too painful. Instead, he lay motionless.

"Must be in a hospital room somewhere," he thought. Again he tried to move his head to see if there was a nurse around. He couldn't see anything and, boy, it was definitely better *not* to move his head. His arm hurt, too. It must have been the way he fell.

He tried to sit up. Every movement was an effort; every bone in his body seemed to ache and there was a terrible tightness in his chest. He levered himself up onto one elbow and looked around the room. There was nothing there. Just him, dressed in a white robe, in a bed draped in white sheets. Nothing else. Nothing. No cabinet with a water jug, no mirror, no chart at the bottom of his bed, no name above his head. Nothing. What sort of place was this?

He lay back for a minute or two to rest; taking time to regain his breath. Then he swung his legs over the side of the bed. He'd never been one to take anything lying down and he wasn't about to start now. He'd struggle out into the corridor and find a nurse or a doctor. There must be someone who could help him in this godforsaken place.

He staggered towards the door, his head swimming.

"Jeez – wonder how long I've been out for?" he thought. "I feel as though I've been hit by a sledgehammer."

He made his way into the corridor, holding onto the white walls for support.

There was no nurses' station, no reception area, no other patients. Just one huge, long, sterile corridor. He made his way along it, for what seemed like miles.

"Don't have much choice, do I?" he thought. "I could lie on the bed and rot or try and find out what's going on." Finally, after what seemed like an eternity, he came to a door which bore one word: enter.

"At last," thought Hank as he pushed the door open.

He really had no idea what he had expected to find behind the door. However, he did know for sure that it wasn't the sight which now greeted him. He also knew for sure that he would never forget the stench that filled his nostrils. He knew that smell. He'd been close to it enough times to recognise it. It was the smell of death.

Just inside the door, standing far too close-by for comfort, was a guy at least six-and-a-half feet tall. He was dressed from head to toe in a long, black, hooded cloak. Hank was unable to see his face as the hood of the cloak was pulled so far down over his head. He held a scythe in his left hand and seemed to float just about an inch or so above the ground, making him seem even taller.

Hank's gaze then drifted to what looked like a row of judges. The judge nearest Hank was grotesque. There was no other way to describe him. He looked as though he had been mauled by a lion, torn from limb to limb and yet survived the attack. Folds of flesh hung from his face. Empty sockets seemed to stare at Hank from where eyes should have been. Part of his left arm was eaten away and his right arm looked like it was going through the last painful stages of gangrene.

Hank was afraid to look further along the bench. When he *did* look, he knew he'd been right to be reluctant. The next judge was white. If Hank had thought his room had looked white and sterile, that had been nothing in comparison to this guy.

His black suit did nothing to help his pallor; he looked as though all his blood had been sucked out of him. His long bony fingers were clutching a gavel. This led Hank to believe that he must be in charge.

He was tall and incredibly thin, with small, beady eyes which seemed to penetrate Hank's very soul. His papery, white skin was stretched tight behind his ears and his ghostly smile revealed pointed, vampire-like teeth.

Hank shivered and moved on down the row. The next two judges looked identical. Hank decided, after he'd had a good look, that they must be twins. Both wore long, black, leather coats, cropped black hair and cowboy boots. On further inspection, Hank saw that each of them held a machine gun.

Neither of the twins had looked at Hank as he entered the room but now they both turned towards him. Hank flinched.

Both had horrific burns on one side of their faces. He realised that the only thing that distinguished one from the other was that while one was scarred down the right hand side; the other was scarred down the left hand side. Each of them had one good eye, the other was merely an empty socket.

Their cheeks were so blistered that pus was running down their faces and dripping onto the bench in front of them. Hank felt sick and looked away.

"What is this place…?" he began.

"You have not yet been given permission to speak," hissed the white judge. As he opened his mouth to speak, the redness of his tongue contrasted starkly with his white skin.

"Permission?" began Hank. "Since when did I ever need…"

"Silence in the court," the white one repeated.

Hank shut up. He knew when he was beaten

and these guys were giving him the creeps. Big time. He staggered backwards and almost fell into the chair that had been placed behind him.

One of the twins turned towards Hank, fixing him with a stare from his one good eye.

"Hank Kane, you have been brought before the Court of Ghouls to answer for crimes committed in life. You have been tried and found guilty and we are here to pass sentence."

"Hey, wait a minute, guilty of what?" Hank tried to jump to his feet. "A guy's innocent till proven guilty and you haven't proved anything. I haven't even had a trial..."

The tall guy with the scythe, who Hank had realised must be none other than *The Grim Reaper* floated over towards him. He pushed Hank none too gently back into his seat and told him to be quiet. "Chill out, man, show a bit of respect," he said, as he floated back to his place at the side of the bench.

The judge on the left spoke for the first time and Hank wished he hadn't bothered.

"As my fellow judge was trying to say, before you so rudely interrupted, you have been tried and found guilty of cheating on police cases. I'm sure you know what we mean: planting evidence, forcing confessions, that type of thing. On many occasions, I might add."

The folds of skin flapped around the side of his face, like dog's ears, as he spoke. Hank stared at him in fascination. This must be some sort of weird dream. No one who looked like that could still be alive. Now the man was using his fingers, that were covered in blood, to pull back the folds of skin from his face.

"Your sentence for cheating, Captain, or should I say, *former* Captain Kane, is to go back to life and solve a case… by the book."

"What do you mean? Go *back* to life? Where are we now? What are you talking about?" Hank protested.

The Grim Reaper sighed and again made his way over to where Hank sat. The second of the twins spoke this time. "Okay, let him see," he signalled.

The Grim Reaper pulled back Hank's robe from his shoulders and motioned for Hank to look down.

"Hey, keep your hands off me! What do you think you're doing?" Hank wished he'd wake up soon. This was just too weird.

"Hank, Hank, Hank," murmured The Grim

Reaper softly. "Look at yourself, Hank. You were shot, remember. You died out on the street and now you've been delivered to us. We have to deal with you now. Help you atone for your past life. Why even a child knows that planting evidence is not what detectives should be doing. So now you have to pay."

Hank summoned the courage to look down at his body. Shaking, he placed his fingers gingerly over a gaping hole in his chest. He must have been shot in the back and the bullet had exited through his heart.

He suddenly realised that all his flesh seemed to be slowly disintegrating! He could see the outline of his bones poking through his skin! Then, little by little, they tore through as the skin disappeared!

But he felt no pain and he certainly didn't feel dead! He wasn't dead. He couldn't be. This wasn't the way he'd imagined it would happen. He had too much to live for – too many crooks still to catch.

"Yes, lots of criminals still to be caught," agreed twin number one, as though reading Hank's mind. "However, they must be caught *honestly* and not by planting evidence."

"What do you mean, 'planting'?" protested Hank. "I never planted evidence on anybody. That's a dirty insinuation you're making and I bet you can't back it up."

"Oh, but we can," drooled the white one, blood dripping from his teeth as he spoke.

"And you say *I've* got bad habits!" thought Hank as he looked away in disgust.

"What about poor Johnny Malcolm then?" sneered the half-eaten judge. "Are you trying to say that you didn't frame him. That you didn't tamper with the forensic evidence?"

Hank said nothing.

"Anyway," the judge continued, "you're not here to defend yourself. You've been tried and found guilty, and we're here to pass sentence."

The other judges nodded in agreement.

Hank wished he had a handkerchief to pass to the judge whose flesh seemed to be rotting from his face as he spoke. Large pools of blood and yellow poison gathered on the bench.

He spoke again. "Your punishment, Kane, is to be sent back to life. There you will return to your former task of solving crime, though this time as a Private Detective. You will clean up some of the pond scum which exists down there. There will, however, be a few conditions which may make things a little more... shall we say... challenging?" The judge reached for a piece of yellowed paper and began to read the conditions:

"Number one: You are now dead. All that's left of your body is a skeleton. However, you'll be glad to hear that we have prepared a chemical compound which, if drunk, will allow flesh to appear on your bones. This compound only works at night so all of your detective work must be carried out during the hours of darkness.

"Number two: You are not allowed to cheat nor are you trusted to solve cases on your own. You must take on an assistant, a boy, and it will be his task to solve the cases for you. You will guide him, as necessary, but on *no account* are you allowed to solve the case for him. You must train this boy so that he is able to solve the cases *honestly*. We will be watching to ensure you don't cheat."

"But I *always* work on my own..." protested Hank, trying to get back on his feet, "I don't need a partner."

The Grim Reaper pushed him back down again. "Take the weight off, buddy."

"Finally, you should know that time passes

much more quickly when you die than it does in life. You have now been dead…" he checked his watch, "… for fifty years. So, let's see, when we send you back, you will be going back to the year 2003."

"Fifty years!" spluttered Hank, "but it was only this morning…"

The Grim Reaper piped up, "Time flies when you're enjoying yourself, eh?" he chuckled. "Look pal, if you can't do the time, don't do the crime. You of all people should appreciate that."

Hank's head was spinning, barely understanding what was being said. But he knew it wasn't good news!

The judge with the rotting flesh looked at the twins enquiringly. "Where shall we drop this former human being, fellas?"

"Oh yes, this is our favourite part," both twins smirked. One rubbed his hands gleefully. The other reached into a drawer for a globe. He placed the globe on his desk and picked up a pin. He spun the globe and when it had stopped spinning, he closed his eyes and stuck the pin in it.

"Glasgow!" he announced, grinning and looking very pleased with himself.

"Not sure where that is," laughed the other

twin. "Somewhere in Europe?" he suggested.

"Scotland," said the white one, glad of the opportunity to establish his authority. "Do you like the sunshine, Kane?" he asked.

Unsure how to answer, Hank replied, "sorta."

"Well," continued the white one, "I just hope you can remember how sunshine felt, 'cause you sure as hell won't get any in Glasgow!"

All the judges roared with laughter. In fact the white one laughed so much that he began to cough and splutter in a terrible manner. The Clerk Of The Court hastily poured blood into a glass from the jug that sat on the judges' bench. He offered the glass to the white one who gratefully sipped it while thanking the clerk for his concern.

The Grim Reaper opened the door and Hank was lifted from his chair and pushed out into the corridor. He could still hear the judges shouting, "Don't forget your umbrella or you'll get soaked… to the bone! Ha, ha, ha!"

"But…" Hank began. "I have questions to ask; too many things I don't understand. Where's this chemical drink? Where are my clothes? Where's my skin?"

The Grim Reaper sighed and led Hank down

the corridor. "Any questions you have should be directed at me."

Hank looked at him in surprise. 'You? Why you?"

"Well here's the worst news, for both of us, my friend… I'm coming with you!"

CHAPTER SIX

"HOME SWEET HOME"

Gordon Street, Glasgow, 2003

LATE one wet afternoon, Hank and The Grim Reaper (TG for short) were making their way towards Gordon Street in Glasgow. The chill of the evening was beginning to set in and Hank pulled his coat collar further up around his neck.

His loss of weight since he had met with his fate wasn't helping much; the flesh was literally falling from his bones. He kept forgetting he was dead and found the experience of catching his reflection in passing shop windows a bit unnerving, to say the least.

On the way to Glasgow, Hank had attracted more than a few puzzled glances from passers by. TG had attracted no attention at all but he put this down to the fact that he could make himself invisible whenever he felt like it!

The journey to Hank's new office in Gordon Street was largely uneventful, thanks to the fact that the sight of a weird looking guy isn't that unusual in that part of town.

TG tried to make conversation but Hank, being

dead, was a little distracted. It was fast becoming obvious to Hank that, in his new situation, TG was possibly his only friend, not an ideal state of affairs!

"Take this," said TG, shoving an odd looking bottle into Hank's pocket. "When we get to the office you'll need a good strong swig of what's inside it." Hank was in too much of a daze to care and he just drifted along the pavement.

"Look, my friend," started TG, "I didn't make this situation, you did and I don't want to be here anymore than you do. But it's no good staying in a huff with the world. You've got work to do."

"Looks like it," grumbled Hank, "but don't expect me to jump for joy just yet..."

"I don't expect you to jump at all. In fact, it's not an activity I'd advise skeletons to indulge in!" laughed TG.

"Well, I guess one of us has to be the joker," moaned Hank, on hearing TG's attempt at humour, "and to think I felt I'd be in awe of you."

"And you're not?" asked TG, a little disappointed. "Wait until you see your new office. You might be a little bit more impressed with me."

It wasn't long before they reached a doorway.

"Here we are," said TG, "home sweet home." He produced a key from underneath his heavy cloak and turned it in the lock of the outer building. He and Hank stepped inside. Hank was indeed impressed.

"Hey, Grim, this looks really familiar," he drawled, removing his hat and tossing it expertly onto the nearby hat-stand. "Looks just like my office back home."

"Yip, that was part of the deal," agreed TG. "I had to recreate your office just as you remembered it, so you wouldn't feel out of place, you know. After all, it's hard for skeletons to feel at home anywhere, other than in a coffin!" Again TG laughed at his own joke and waited in vain for Hank to join in. When Hank didn't, the smile on TG's face died. His expression changed to one of exasperation.

"D'ya have any idea, Hank, the amount of trouble I had to go to to find some of this junk… err... I mean 'stuff'? Most of it I got from some strange market, that people here call 'Ra Barras'. You'd be amazed at that place." TG reached under his cloak and pulled out a Walkman and some CDs, "Check these out," he said.

Hank looked quizzically at the alien-looking goods TG had thrust into his hands.

"What the hell is all this stuff?"

"Oh, yeah, I forgot. You were dead while all this stuff was being invented. I'll explain another time. Got them all for a tenner. Not bad, huh? The guy wanted fifteen quid. Didn't know who he was dealing with. Told him to take a good look at my face, then offered a tenner."

"A what?"

"A tenner. Ten pounds is a tenner. Forget dollars, Hank, it's pounds they use here, or 'quids', which is another name for pounds."

Hank put the Walkman and CDs back into TG's hands and looked at him sullenly.

"You were ripped off. Sure hope *I* don't waste as many 'tenners' as you."

TG ignored the insolence. There was no insult he hadn't heard a million times.

"The Court Of Ghouls gave me a very limited budget to kit this dump out. I spent it all wisely; saved them a fortune."

"How considerate of the Court of Ghouls," said Hank wryly. Suddenly he looked at TG like he'd looked at a thousand con men.

"My guess is that the fortune you saved has still

to find its way back to the Court. You got receipts for all this stuff?"

The Grim Reaper walked over to Hank and put his arm around his shoulder. "Hank, Hank, Hank. I know you're a good detective but we all know your reputation. Why, I've even 'collected' the souls of the poor saps you sent to the chair and I think they were more scared of you than they were of me. But here's the thing, my smart friend: it's me who holds all the cards now. Now the law's on *my* side. So what if I like my personal stereo, a bit of Hip Hop never did no harm, man. The point is that if I don't like you, buddy, I can lose you in a dark hole – and you could be lost for a very, long time. There are a lot of people you can afford to upset. But, I ain't one of them."

For the first time in his life, Hank felt completely powerless. He felt the same way criminals felt when they realised their fate was completely in Hank Kane's hands. Only this time, Hank Kane's hands held nobody's fate, not even his own. He felt empty and fell silent, trying to hide his helplessness from TG. But, as Hank discovered, nothing can be kept hidden from The Grim Reaper.

"My guess, if I can borrow your own expression,

Hank, is that you now understand this new situation. Don't worry, it's in my interest to help you. It reflects well on me. Besides, I like my wee 'business trips' and the 'expenses opportunities' they present.

"You guessed right, not all the money I save goes back to the court. C'mon, what are they gonna do with it? Hank, I'll take all your wise cracks, all your insults. No problem. But don't ever interfere with the way I make a living, OK?"

"Jeez," observed Hank, "you're beginning to sound like The Godfather." But Hank didn't scare easily. After all, he *was* dead. How much worse could it get? Still, he made a mental note that TG's finances were none of his business. "We got a deal, Grim. So, I guess if I need something for my office, all I need to do is ask?"

TG looked at Hank with a slight smile. "You wouldn't be foolish enough to blackmail *me*, the Grimmest of all Reapers, would you, Hank?"

"No, I've put away more blackmailers than I care to remember. Let's just say, if I ever ask you for something, it's only 'cause it will help me solve a case. And that helps you, right?"

The Grim Reaper looked at Hank, wondering how it was that he suddenly found himself compromised by this crooked cop. He realised that he was now working with someone who was pretty smart. The slight smile grew into a full blown one.

"We got a deal, Hank," said TG, extending his hand, which Hank shook.

Hank took a good look around the room. The office did indeed look homely. It was a bit like something from a Humphrey Bogart movie: old-fashioned black telephone, humming fan slowly spinning on the ceiling, blinds on the window, oblong spotlight on the desk. In fact, the only unfamiliar thing was a constant pitter-patter sound on the windows outside. Rain was not something Hank had had a lot of experience of in Los Angeles. His instincts told him he'd be a lot more used to it by the end of this case.

Hank sat down at the desk and put his feet up. "Bit warmer in here than it is out there," he observed.

"Yeah, I even imported some of that Los Angeles summer air. Told ya I pulled out all the stops," boasted TG.

Still looking unimpressed, Hank ventured, "I'll need wheels. *My* wheels. I used to have the best darn car in LA."

TG grimaced a little and then his face relaxed. "I'm owed a few favours, I suppose."

"Might need some gas."

"Petrol, Hank. Petrol's what they call it here. And my guess is that your 'wheels' will need more than petrol." TG paused to think. "What's the expiry date on your credit card, Hank?"

"My what?"

"Never mind. Looks like I'll be funding your detective work. Hope you don't become a financial drain on my resources, Hank."

Hank realised that he needed TG to be his banker as much as his friend.

"Grim, I'll appreciate all the help you're gonna give me. Any advice for a newly dead detective?"

"Yeah," replied TG, "keep all your receipts."

Hank began to loosen his collar and was shocked to see that his hands were by now almost skeletal, indeed there was very little flesh left on any part of his body.

Hank went over to the blinds on the window and parted them. It was dark outside. Time for a drink from the bottle TG had given him earlier. He put the bottle on his desk, almost smiling at the Court of Ghouls' use of the skull and crossbones on the label. Almost immediately, he felt the flesh starting to cover his bones and was pleased to look in the mirror and see his human form returning. The skeletal look wasn't in the least flattering.

"Remember to be careful of how much of that stuff you drink," advised TG, "it's to be used sparingly and only at night. No point in using it during the day," he continued, "it will only make you look 'normal' during the hours of darkness."

"Yeah, yeah," drawled Hank impatiently. He hated being lectured about anything. "What about my so-called 'assistant'? Where am I supposed to find him? Not that I need one, you understand, I prefer to work alone. Why can't you just take me over to 'the other side' TG? You don't need to go along with what the Court says. Just let me pass over. I am dead, after all, and I really don't want to spend eternity wandering about the streets of Glasgow looking for criminals."

"Sorry, Hank, no can do. And, hey, how do you think I feel? I'm gonna be The Grim Reaper forever! No prospects, lousy pay and long hours. I have to work 24/7 and I have no say in it whatsoever. So stop complaining."

"Get a life, TG, and leave me alone," said Hank.

He'd had just about enough for one day. He swung around in his chair to look out of the window, deliberately turning his back on TG.

"I can't leave you alone, Hank, you know that buddy," smirked TG. "Let's just get on and make the most of it. Your assistant will attend for interview tomorrow night at eight pm. He's applying for the job right about…" he checked his watch "… now, I should think. Bright little guy, should put you to shame."

Hank refused to comment, instead putting a 1953 copy of *The Los Angeles Times* newspaper (thoughtfully provided by TG) over his face and settling down for forty winks. Just before he dozed off, he suddenly noticed the front page headline:

"HANK KANE SHOT DEAD!" it screamed, just under the date 'July 1st 1953'.

"Yup," he said to TG, "you definitely got a sense of humour!"

CHAPTER SEVEN

THE "KID" RIDES INTO TOWN

Somewhere in Glasgow

CHARLIE Christian was bored. Not just bored in the way that you can't decide whether to watch TV or switch on your *Playstation*, but bored to the extent that he had decided to talk to his little sister.

Now that's *really* bored.

"Alright, Ace?" he said as he pushed open her bedroom door.

"What do you want?" she retorted, looking up from her diary. "And my name's Annie. I'm not some character in one of your dumb detective books."

"Annie, Ace, whatever. What do you get to write in that diary of yours? It's not like your life is interesting." He sat down on the edge of her bed and squinted to see what she had written.

She covered the small pink book protectively. "None of your business, Charlie Christian, and if I ever find out you've been reading it behind my back I'll tell Mum."

"'I'll tell Mum'," Charlie mimicked as he got up and left the room. He wasn't *that* bored after all, he decided.

He and his little sister and their mum had recently moved house so that they could be nearer Mum's job. She was a nurse who had got shift work in the local hospital. Charlie hadn't minded the move; only thing was there hadn't been much time as yet to make any friends at school, so he was at a bit of a loose end at the moment.

Detective stories were Charlie's obsession. The bookcase in his bedroom was crammed full of them, each of them dog-eared through constant reading and re-reading over the years.

Annie poked fun at him as he could usually be found somewhere reading one of his detective stories for the hundredth time. She secretly admired his detective skills (though she would rather have died than tell him that). She'd seen his skills put to use on the odd occasion at home and she'd even seen him solving minor thefts and stuff at school.

Charlie went into his bedroom and lay down to read last month's copy of *Detective Monthly*. Ever since Mum had allowed him to subscribe to this magazine, he'd bombarded its editor with sleuthing suggestions, detective stories, competition ideas and loads more stuff. He flicked through the advertisement section at the back, even though he'd read it a dozen times already.

He was really surprised to come across a full-page advertisement that he hadn't seen before. It was from a detective seeking an assistant!

That's so weird, thought Charlie. Didn't spot that the last time I read this page.

The ad was for an assistant to a Private Detective who was operating in the centre of Glasgow. Thrilled, Charlie cut out the application form, which had to be completed and sent to the address given. He filled in the application: name, age, experience (he elaborated a bit there, but then who wouldn't?). Although he knew he'd missed the post, he still put it in the letterbox that night.

The next day, Charlie knew for definite that there was something very strange about this detective agency. He'd posted the application form after the last post the previous night but a reply was delivered to him in the post that morning! He went into the kitchen and read it.

It said:

> Please attend an interview (see address below) at 8 pm tomorrow evening. Detective Hank Kane will see you. Kindly be on time.

Underneath was written:

> Anyone with a love of pipes, magnifying glasses and deerstalker hats need not attend.

That's a bit sarky, thought Charlie, smiling in spite of himself. He began to think about how he could get to the interview. Mum was on nightshift for the next few weeks, so she wouldn't realise if he sneaked out. However, he just knew she'd go mad if he mentioned interviews at eight o'clock at night (and he had to admit it was a bit weird).

He decided he better come clean. After all, he was supposed to be responsible for Ace when Mum was working despite the fact that once his sister was asleep, it would be easier to wake the dead.

He called his mum on her mobile. As he selected

her name he was already thinking of ways of persuading her to let him go to the interview. She knew Charlie was destined to be a detective of some sort. Everyone did. And she'd have to agree that this job would help his future career. "Anyway," thought Charlie, "if she says 'no' and hangs up, I'll just have to keep ringing her until she says 'yes'!"

At the end of the call, Charlie was far from happy. The condition on which he was allowed go was that his mum came along, too. But hey, at least he was going to the interview. And at least he didn't have to bring Ace along, despite Mum thinking that would be a great idea! He'd have to keep it a secret from Ace, otherwise she'd throw a right fit.

He got a cold juice from the fridge and reached into the cupboard for some peanuts. He picked up one of his favourite detective books and turned to chapter eleven. It was the one where the detective announces who the murderer is. He took a handful of nuts and sighed contentedly; his day had brightened considerably.

* * * * * * *

At seven-thirty the following evening, Annie was asleep in her room, the sitter had arrived and Mum was ready to go. Charlie crept down the hallway and could hear Annie snuffling lightly as he walked past her bedroom door.

"I'll be back before she even knows I've been out," he thought.

Charlie whistled as himself and his mum walked down rain-soaked West Nile Street. Underneath the umbrella they shared, they discussed what Mr Hank Kane might be like. They wouldn't have much longer to wait to find out, Charlie thought to himself.

They reached Gordon Street and looked from left to right to see which direction the office lay in. They found it fairly easily (using Charlie's detective skills) and desperate to get out of the pelting rain, they quickly pushed open the heavy outer door. They went down a small hallway, then knocked on a door. The top of the door was made of glass and bore the words:

PRIVATE DETECTIVE
HANK KANE
KNOCK & ENTER

So they knocked and entered. "Wow!" Charlie couldn't help the word escaping from his lips. Both himself and his mum felt as though they'd travelled back in time by at least fifty years. "Bogey eat your heart out!" Charlie exclaimed as he examined the interior of the office.

"Goodness!" exclaimed Mrs Christian. "They must have money to burn with the heating turned up so high. My, it's so stuffy!"

Hank entered from a small washroom to the right of his office. He'd just been checking his flesh in the mirror the way most people check their hair. His shirtsleeves were rolled up and he was fidgeting with his braces.

"Must get that heating fixed," he muttered, in an attempt to explain the warm temperature.

Charlie and his mum turned towards Hank. They saw a tall good-looking man, wearing what looked to Charlie like very dated clothes. His mum recognised them as being from the 1950s. The man was wearing black trousers, a shirt that must have been white once, and a thin, strip of a tie.

He looked like a detective from a black and white movie. His gauntness made him seem even taller than he was and his cheeks were hollowed and his eyes heavy-lidded. And of course, he had a world-weary expression; the essential trademark of the detective.

Hank strolled towards Charlie and extended his hand, "Mr Christian, I presume."

Charlie shook Hank's hand. "That's me. Cool! You're an American, right? Related to Humphrey Bogart, by any chance?"

"Bogie a friend of yours, is he?" asked Hank, pleased that he'd been given the chance to be sarcastic so early on in the conversation. He liked to discourage all unnecessary chitchat.

Hank glanced at the kid just to make sure he'd hit the mark. He hadn't. "Not exactly shy and retiring, are we?" observed Hank, as he indicated the chairs they should sit on. He only nodded at Charlie's mum. He couldn't risk offering to shake hands with her. He wasn't sure if his flesh would stay on his hand.

"So do you know any detectives who are shy and retiring?" asked Charlie. "You don't get anywhere in this trade if you don't ask questions," he continued, ignoring his mother's glare.

"And you've been 'in the trade' for how long?'" asked Hank, as he sat down on the other side of the desk.

"Oh Mr Kane," started Mrs Christian, "Charlie's just tailor-made for this type of work. And besides, a wee Saturday job is just what he needs and…"

"Mrs Christian," interrupted Hank, "this ain't no Saturday job. I make the hours up as I go along, or should I say, the case does. I understand the kid's on school holidays. I hope to have the case finished by next term. But, matters of life and death don't run to no time-table, doll."

"No, no of course not," replied Charlie's mum, attempting to take expressions like "life and death" and "doll" in her stride. She'd do anything not to mess this up for Charlie.

Charlie of course, lived and breathed such expressions night and day. As he sat down he'd noticed the bottle bearing the skull and crossbones. Not a soft drink, then, he thought, more curious than worried.

Charlie continued, "Well, I'm not exactly 'in the trade', if you see what I mean, but I'm very interested in detective work. I've read almost every crime novel ever written; know all the best crime movies…"

Hank held up his hand. "Okay, okay, stop right there. Next thing you'll be spouting *quotes* from old movies."

Charlie grinned. "Well, now that you mention it…"

Hank held up his hand again. "This is serious, kid. I'm looking for an assistant and you've been recommended."

Charlie opened his mouth to ask who'd recommended him but Hank shook his head and said, "You don't wanna know, kid, believe me. Now we got a case to crack so you come along for the ride; we'll see how you work out and we'll take it from there. You can start right away."

"Are you kidding?" asked Charlie in astonishment. "That's it? You mean I got the job?"

Hank poured the strongest looking coffee Charlie had ever seen or smelt, into a cup. Hank drank the sticky tar-like coffee in one go and sighed.

"That'll kill you, you know," said Charlie.

Hank laughed. "If you only knew, kid, if you only knew."

"Hey, stop calling me 'kid'. My name's Charlie. And I'm *not* a kid. I'm twelve years old."

He lifted a photograph from beside the ancient looking telephone, trying not to listen to his mother telling him to leave it alone.

"Put that down, kid," said Hank, ignoring

Charlie's request to stop calling him 'kid'. "Where's your manners? It's rude to pick up things that don't belong to you."

Charlie looked at the old photograph of a famous American baseball player and whistled in admiration. "Joe Di Maggio! Cool! And it's autographed too."

Mrs Christian tried hard to look like she too recognised the man in the photo but decided not to say anything.

Hank smiled in spite of himself. "So you recognise one of the greats when you see him? Doesn't make you no detective though. So, you follow baseball, kid or what?"

"Err, no. Baseball is not exactly the sport of the day in Scotland. Celtic? Rangers? Football? Maybe you'd know it as 'soccer'?" Hank looked blankly at Charlie. It was as if the kid was talking Chinese. He shook his head and motioned to the photo Charlie still held in his hand. "Put that back before you drop the darn thing. We got work to do."

Charlie and his mum sat back to listen.

"We got a new case, a Mr..." Hank looked at the scrawls on his notepad, "... Joe Jackson. Called in earlier tonight. Seems his brother George died recently and he thinks the cops ain't movin' fast enough on the case. Jackson believes his brother was killed, though the cops seem to be going for accidental death, so he wants us involved."

Charlie put his hands behind his head and copied Hank's pose of putting his feet on top of the desk, giving every impression of expertly mulling over the case.

Hank pushed his feet off the desk. "Keep 'em on the floor, kid. It's *my* desk."

Charlie did so, grudgingly. Better keep his nose clean for the time being, he supposed, if he wanted to keep this exciting new job. Plus, his mother would go mental if he embarrassed her any more.

"George Jackson, the dead guy, lived with his wife on the outskirts of the city. They ran a taxi company: private cars, wedding cars, that sort of thing. Always been money in the family. Parents left a fair bit when they died. According to the brother, they were doing really well; had bought a villa in Spain, the wife had regular shopping trips in New York, weekends in Paris. Not what you'd call poor."

Charlie tried to look intelligent. Truth be told, he was almost over-awed by the whole thing. Half an hour ago he'd been plain old Charlie

Christian. Now here he was assisting Private Detective Hank Kane on a murder case! Cool or what!

"I'm really on a case, Mum!" he whispered. "Wow!"

Mrs Christian felt proud of Charlie but also a little worried. Somehow though, she trusted Hank. There was something about him that made her feel comfortable with all of this, despite the fact that he could be quite rude to Charlie. But then sometimes Charlie needed bringing down a peg or two.

Charlie cleared his throat in what he hoped was a manly sort of way and tried to adopt Hank's casual pose. "Did they have any children?"

"Nope, no kids. Just the two of them. Hadn't been married that long; couple of years or so. According to the brother they were very happy. Word is that George, the deceased, died of a heart attack. Found him face down in the garden pond. Police seem to think he had a heart attack while he was feeding the ornamental goldfish. Just fell over and landed face down in the pond. Death from drowning. Wife's very upset apparently and having a hard time coming to terms with it. She's leaning very hard on Joe for support. Joe's the brother, the guy who came to see me," explained Hank again, in case Charlie was losing the plot.

"I know, I know," said Charlie, secretly glad that Hank had explained again, as he'd been getting a bit confused. "So who's running the business?" asked Charlie, hoping it was a relevant question.

"Joe is," replied Hank. "He worked alongside his brother so he knows the ropes. What I reckon we have to do now is call on Mrs Jackson…" He looked at his notes. "Emily Jackson that is, and get some background on the case. From the detail Joe's given me, I'm not surprised the police are treating it as death by natural causes but he seems to think otherwise. And, quite frankly kid, I'm just not in a position to say 'no' to anyone just now. I have to take on any job that comes my way."

Charlie nodded in agreement. "Yeah, we do, don't we," said Charlie, unaware that Hank's eyes had rolled up to heaven and back down again. "Can I ask you something?"

"Ask away," nodded Hank, bracing himself.

"What's the strange smell in here?"

"It's just a bit musty, been closed for a while," said Hank, hastily. He knew exactly what the kid meant, though he couldn't tell him that. The smell of death hung thick about the place, not necessarily emanating from himself, as he was a relatively fresh corpse, but seeping from every pore of The Grim Reaper.

TG was sitting listening to everything in the room next door but Hank was very aware of the smell of rotting flesh, which was coming from underneath the door.

He checked his watch. "Let's go."

Charlie sat up in surprise. "Now? Go visit her now? But I thought this was just an interview."

Hank sighed. "Look, kid, I interviewed you, you got the job, now we need to start work. You have a problem with that? Got to get home before it's really dark?" This last comment was said with heavy sarcasm.

"No, I don't have a problem," replied Charlie indignantly. "I can stay out as late as I want. Let's go Mr Kane, let's go do some investigating."

Mrs Christian broke her silence. "We'll see about that, young man."

Hank realised that Mrs Christian could pose a problem and that he better deal with it.

"Mrs Christian," he said, unearthing his old charm, "Charlie is in good hands. I'll drop him home in about an hour. Here's my card. I'll call you if there's any change in plan," as he guided her and Charlie out the door.

On their way out the door, Mrs Christian suddenly paused. She'd recognised a substance in a small bowl in the corner of the office. She raised her hand to point to it but Hank stopped her by taking her hand and shaking it.

"Goodbye, Mrs Christian, goodbye." He could see that she was still interested in the contents of the bowl and that he'd have to come clean. "Yes, Mrs C, rats," he acknowledged, "lots of 'em in this office. But that little feast in the bowl will give the little beggars a meal to remember, huh?"

Mrs Christian had stopped listening after the first mention of rats and was almost running out of the room as fast as she could. She was quickly followed by Charlie. She made her way home, hoping she'd never have to go back to Hank's rat-infested office again. Charlie waited outside the office for his new boss.

Just before Hank left the office he popped his head round the door of the room next door and whispered, "Hey, Grim, don't suppose you found my old car?"

"Your carriage awaits outside, sir," replied TG

with a certain amount of pride. He couldn't help adding, "Damn I'm good, very, good, at what I do. Hell, I'm the best!" he said to no-one in particular. TG found that he was alone. Hank had already lifted his hat from the stand and was gone.

CHAPTER EIGHT

THE WIDOW JACKSON

Hank's old and rather run-down chevy pulled into the gravelled driveway of the Jackson mansion. The unlikely pair got out of the car and made their way to the front door.

"What a wreck," moaned Charlie, looking back at the ancient car that he'd nearly been too embarrassed to get into. "Where did you get that... that...?" The word he was looking for was, "heap" but Hank suggested, "Classic Car". As Hank walked towards the Jackson house, Charlie could have sworn he heard his new boss laugh.

A tearful Emily Jackson answered the ringing of the doorbell.

Hank flashed his ID at her quickly, before she noticed it wasn't official police ID.

"She's already spoken to the police," boomed a voice from behind Mrs Jackson. Hank and Charlie looked up and were faced with one of the Jackson family henchmen. The guy was built like a sumo wrestler and he didn't look too happy to see either of them on the doorstep. Beside her henchman Emily Jackson looked small and fragile. But then *anyone* would have looked small and fragile beside Harry the henchman.

"It's okay, Harry, it's okay," she said to the giant of a man, as if talking to a guard dog. She turned her attention to Hank and Charlie. "Come in, come in," she said, leading the way into the sitting room.

The two of them followed her, Charlie very cautiously, trying desperately not to make eye contact with Harry the henchman. The guy was just *too* scary.

Hank and Charlie sat down opposite Mrs Jackson. She offered them coffee but both declined. Charlie had never drunk coffee before in his life but didn't want to look childish by asking for coke. Instead he decided to politely refuse the offer.

"Okay, then, Mrs Jackson," said Hank, taking a small notepad from his pocket, "we know you've been through a very difficult time, but would you mind answering just a few questions?"

Damn it, thought Charlie, I should have thought of taking notes – I look really unprofessional now. He stared at his trainers, disappointed with himself.

Hank started to ask all the usual questions, such

as: “Where were you when it happened? Who found him? Was there anyone who wanted to harm him?”

Emily Jackson answered slowly and painfully, in a voice weakened by grief. “Sounds as though she’s really upset,” thought Charlie. His eyes settled on some flight tickets on top of the coffee table. He leaned forward.

“Excuse me, Mrs Jackson?” he said.

She turned to look at the boy.

“Mind if I have some fruit?” he gestured towards the heavily laden fruit bowl.

“Help yourself, lad, help yourself,” she said, in between bouts of nose blowing and eye wiping.

Charlie pretended to examine the fruit, as if looking for the best piece. All the time his eyes were scanning the tickets.

Glasgow – Paris
2 passengers
Flight times

Where was the date? He couldn’t see the date. He dropped the plum he was holding and took the opportunity to look more closely at the tickets.

Success! The travel date was for a week next Friday. The first named passenger was Mrs E Jackson and the second was…

"Charlie, Mrs Jackson's talking to you," said Hank.

"Oops, sorry," said Charlie, scrambling to his feet. "Sorry, Mrs Jackson, what did you say?"

"I asked if you were all right down there," she said. "You seem to have been scrambling about on the floor for an awfully long time."

Charlie showed her the plum. "Picked the best one, Mrs Jackson, and didn't want to let it get away, that's all." He tried to smile at Hank, but ended up looking like someone who was in pain.

Hank got to his feet, put his notebook in his coat pocket and made his way towards the door of the sitting room.

"Thanks for your time, Mrs Jackson, and sorry to have troubled you." He quickly pulled open the door and Harry the henchman almost fell over. He had stayed in the hall, listening to every word.

"Hope you didn't miss anything," said Hank, as he and Charlie walked through the hall towards the front door. Before Harry had a chance to reply, Hank and Charlie had reached the front door and had closed it firmly behind them.

The two detectives made their way back down the driveway and got into Hank's car.

"What in the name of all that's decent was that little charade about?" Hank spluttered as he started up the engine. "You're supposed to be helping me, listening to what's being said and instead of that you're crawling about the floor like some dumb jerk. I'm presuming you had a reason, kid."

"Hey, I take exception to that," said Charlie in between mouthfuls of plum. "I *was* being observant. I saw something I'll bet you didn't."

He told Hank about the flight tickets. "I was just about to try and see what the second name was when you interrupted me."

"Doesn't prove a thing," said Hank, not taking his eyes off the road. "All it means is that Mrs Emily Jackson is taking a trip to Paris in a week's time. Could be with a friend, could be with a relation. The tickets could have been booked any time, so I don't see the point you're making."

"Well," replied Charlie, "I just thought it might have been a bit suspicious to be going to Paris a week after her husband died. I mean, shouldn't she still be in mourning?"

"Drop you here?" asked Hank, ignoring him and pulling the car over to the side of the road.

"Great," said Charlie unenthusiastically. Hank had disregarded everything he'd just said. He knew he wasn't a super sleuth but he *was* trying. Hank could at least act like he was grateful.

He got out of the car and started to cross the road towards his house. He didn't even bother turning around to wave.

CHAPTER NINE

SOMETHING IN THE CELLAR

A couple of nights later, Charlie decided to pay another visit to the Jackson home. He had heard nothing from Hank and thought he may as well go back to the house to see if there was any evidence he could pick up.

He was determined to show Hank that he could be just as good a detective as the next person, if not better. He had noticed on their previous visit to the house that there was a cellar and the window hadn't looked all that secure.

Charlie got to the house at about nine o'clock. It was just about dark enough for him to creep through the bushes in the garden and make his way to the cellar.

It was just as he thought. The window was ever so slightly ajar, and he was able to push it open just far enough for him to climb in. Yeuch! He'd made contact with a huge spider's web. He struggled to get the cobwebs off his face and out of his hair as he landed with a soft thump on the floor of the cellar.

It was pitch black inside. He felt something

slimy slide across his face and he brushed at it hastily with his hand. He managed to get it off his face but now it was stuck to his hand! He shivered and shook his hand quickly, trying to dislodge whatever was stuck there. He realised that it was only a slug but it was sticking to him like glue. He placed his hand on the window ledge and dragged it downwards, trying to rid himself of the slimy creature. Success. He felt it drop off and could see the glistening shape clinging to the ledge. He shivered again and moved away.

He hadn't brought his flashlight with him, knowing that if he were to shine a light someone would see it. His eyes would soon get used to the darkness. He made his way gingerly across the floor, trying to feel his way and trying hard not to stumble and make a noise.

He could hear the shuffling of rats as they made their nightly journey across the wooden floorboards, foraging for food. All he could do was try and shut the sound from his mind. Though he wouldn't admit it to anyone, he was terrified of rats, spiders, and creepy crawlies in general.

His sister, Ace, was much braver than he was;

he'd seen her pick up spiders from the bath. She'd even spent a whole summer catching as many insects as she could. She'd kept them in a variety of boxes and jars in her bedroom. Charlie had avoided going into her room all that summer, thinking up the most elaborate of excuses when his mum asked him to go in for one reason or another.

He heard a noise behind him, louder than rats this time. He thought he could hear breathing and he froze. He realised that he wasn't alone. Someone was in the cellar with him. He'd have to move quickly. He could just make out the outline of a small staircase on his right. He made his way over there, crouching beneath the stairway and pulling his legs underneath him. He tried to hold his breath.

He could definitely hear someone else breathing and whoever it was was heading in his direction. Damn, someone must have seen me come in here.

"I wasn't careful enough," he thought. He tried to make himself even smaller.

The footsteps drew nearer. Charlie curled into an even tighter ball and closed his eyes. "If I ever get out of this situation," he promised himself, "I'll give up detective work forever."

His eyes had become accustomed to the dark so he opened them and dared himself to look more closely at the approaching feet. He recognised those trainers. He put out a hand and grabbed a leg.

Ace let out a muffled screech.

Charlie sprung out of his hiding place and quickly placed a hand over her mouth.

"Sshhh," he whispered. "What are you doing here? Why are you following me?"

Ace pushed his hand away. "You're hurting me," she hissed. "I saw you sneaking out, so I decided to come, too. It's a free world, you know."

"Yeah, and it's also a very dangerous world," said Charlie, "and you have no idea what you're getting into. You had no right following me here and Mum would go ape if she knew where you were."

Ace half smiled in the darkness. "Why don't you tell her then?"

Charlie said nothing.

"See, you can't, 'cause you know you'll incriminate yourself and have to explain what you were doing here."

Charlie shook his head. What had he ever done to deserve a sister? He'd sort this out later but right now he had work to do. He told Ace to hide under the stairs and wait for him to come back.

"Stay right there," he told her. "You're not to come out till I say so. This is man's work."

Annie sighed. Charlie was sooo pathetic at times. Pretending to be all macho and protective when he wouldn't even go into the shower if there was a creepy crawly in there. She moved her position slightly. She could feel the damp from the floorboards seeping through her body. Maybe this hadn't been such a good idea after all.

Charlie left Annie under the stairs and crept back across the room. His right shoe suddenly made contact with something sharp and he stifled a cry. He looked down and could just about make out the shape of a chainsaw. He bent down and wiped his finger along one of the large teeth. He could feel some kind of dried liquid on it. Could it be blood, he thought to himself?

But what would a blood-soaked chainsaw be doing in the cellar? He couldn't think of an ordinary reason. He could feel the tiny hairs on the back of his neck standing up and he tried to talk sense to himself. Maybe it's not blood. "Even if it is blood, it could have been used to cut anything," he thought, trying to convince himself. Who says it had to be something human?

He stopped at the far end of the cellar. A huge box was taking up almost the whole length of one wall. The last thing Charlie felt like doing was trying to open up the box and see what was inside. He had a feeling that whatever was in there wouldn't be pleasant. In fact the only thing stopping him from fleeing was the thought of Hank laughing at him when he told him the story.

There seemed to be a lid on the box so Charlie put his fingertips under it. He began easing it upwards and as he did so a shaft of light shone out from it. It seemed to be some kind of giant freezer. Lifting the lid was heavy work but by using both hands he managed to prop it up against the wall. Now he could see the contents.

Charlie leaned in and poked a few items around with his hands. There were a couple of huge frozen pizzas, big bags of peas and carrots and about ten blocks of ice cream. Charlie lifted up one of the frozen pizzas and saw a plastic bag underneath. He put the pizza aside and picked up the bag.

It was difficult to make out what was in it. Some

kind of meat? Lamb chops? Steak? It looked like it had some kind of hair on it. Charlie turned it upside down and examined it more closely under the light from the lid.

He could see something that looked like a marble. He breathed on the bag and tried to defrost what was inside so that he could see it more clearly. He rubbed his finger over the plastic. Suddenly he knew exactly what he was looking at. There was no doubt about it. It was a human eye.

Charlie dropped the bag in shock. It fell to the bottom of the freezer, dislodging a number of other bags on its way. Charlie felt as if the contents of his stomach were rising up into his mouth. The freezer was full of what Charlie could now see, all too clearly, were human body parts.

Before he even had a chance to react, he heard the door of the cellar opening and footsteps coming down a flight of stairs. He was still so dazed by the grisly discovery in the freezer that he barely even felt two large hands grabbing him by the collar. He was hoisted into the air and pushed down into the bottom of the freezer. The lid was slammed shut and a bolt shot across.

Charlie found himself sharing a freezer with the pieces of a human corpse.

* * * * * * *

Five minutes later, Harry the henchman stood at the top of the steps to the cellar. Emily Jackson was with him. "I knew they were trouble," Harry was muttering as he struggled to find the light switch. Emily Jackson, very much in control, was already hurrying down the steps. She was no longer the weak, fragile figure she had presented to Hank and Charlie.

Harry came down the steps behind her and they made their way over towards the freezer. She waited for him to slide the bolt back and lift the lid.

"He's in here," said Harry, lifting the lid with a flourish. Apart from the severed limbs, the freezer was empty.

CHAPTER TEN

MRS WHO?

CHARLIE and Ace were running for their lives down the road. Charlie thought his lungs were going to explode. They rounded a corner and Charlie grabbed Ace's hand. "Bus!" he managed to shout. Both of them practically threw themselves onto the bus. The driver looked at them in amusement. "Someone chasing you?" he joked as he took their fares.

Charlie pocketed his change and himself and Ace flopped down onto two seats. It was only then that Charlie found enough breath to thank Ace for rescuing him from a chilling end.

* * * * * * *

Hank was suffering, or at least his pocket was. He and TG were having a game of poker and it just didn't seem to be Hank's night. He was glad when he heard the outside door slamming and the sound of feet running quickly up the stairs.

TG got up swiftly and floated into the room next door. He was just in time as Charlie and Ace pushed open the door and threw themselves onto two chairs.

"Hey, guys, doin' fine, thanks," said Hank sarcastically. "And don't bother to introduce us," said Hank, nodding in Annie's direction.

Charlie slowed his breathing and tried to relate the night's events to Hank. He reached into his pocket and placed the contents on the desk.

Annie recoiled in horror. Slugs and bugs, maybe, but a severed finger? That was a different matter altogether.

Hank looked down at the finger Charlie had placed on the desk. He raised an eyebrow.

Slowly Charlie recounted his story to Hank, pausing only to introduce Annie and to relate the part she had played in the evening's events.

"We gotta go back there, Hank, before they get rid of the evidence. Emily Jackson, and probably her henchman, are guilty of a pretty horrific crime."

Hank smiled and placed the finger in a small evidence bag he had taken from the drawer in his desk. Charlie noticed that Hank had taken another evidence bag from the same drawer. Hank stood up and shrugged on his coat.

"Let's go, guys, but not to the Jackson home. It's time to pay the local cops a visit."

Puzzled, Charlie and Ace followed Hank out of the office. Charlie looked back and noticed that there were two hands of cards lying on the desk. He wondered who had been playing the second hand of cards. Furthermore, Hank seemed to be taking all this shocking news far too well; almost as if it wasn't news to him at all.

* * * * * * *

Charlie and Ace had almost finished their story. Detective Inspector Brownlow had listened attentively to everything they had to say; taking notes and nodding in the right places. Just before they finished speaking, Hank placed two small bags on the desk in front of the detective. One contained the severed finger and the other, Hank explained, contained rat poison.

"That's how sweet Emily Jackson killed her husband," Hank told them. "She'd been giving him the poison daily, tiny amounts in his food so that he wouldn't notice. This particular type has no taste. When mixed with food it has the effect of weakening the heart, if used over a period of time.

She's an expert, you see, our Mrs Jackson. Or

should I say Mrs Williams, Mrs Cuthbert or even Mrs Langham? She's been married four times, this dame has, or at least four that we know of! Her real name is Emily Alexander, sister of Harry Alexander."

Hank smiled at Charlie. "Yep, Harry the henchman is Emily's brother. Together they've been making a small fortune out of killing off her husbands. She ensnares the unfortunate men, marries them and then gets them to increase their insurance policies. Herself and her brother then either chop them up or poison them, pocketing all the insurance money in the process.

"I think," he looked at the detective, "that if you check, you'll find that what I'm saying is right. Though you'd better call at the house immediately if you want to get there before the evidence is removed. You can hold onto these, obviously," he nodded his head towards the two bags he had placed on the desk.

Hank got up to leave and signalled to Charlie and Annie to join him. Charlie was impressed, but how had Hank known so much about the case?

The three of them left the police station, heading for Hank's car. Annie yawned. It had been a long night, and she was pretty tired. Hank drove along the darkened streets. Charlie sat silently beside him in the passenger seat, Annie in the back.

"Thanks," said Hank as they pulled into the street where Charlie and Annie lived. "You've both been a great help. And you'll make a great detective when you're older, kid."

Charlie felt as though Hank was saying goodbye. "Is that it?" he asked. "Job over? You don't want me any more?"

Hank leant over and opened the door, signalling to Charlie to get out.

"Look, no hard feelings, but, yeah, you're right, the job's over. We've both done what we had to do, K…."

Hank was obviously going to annoy Charlie one last time by calling him "Kid" but he stopped himself, smiled and said: "Charlie, you'll make a hell of a detective. Just remember though, sometimes you might need more help than you think you do." Hank winked at Annie and she winked back.

Charlie got out of the car and looked back at Hank as if he was about to say something but Hank stopped him.

"You know, Charlie, the best way to learn something yourself, is to teach it to someone else."

"Ain't that the truth!" whispered Annie, imitating Hank's world-weary manner. She slid out of the car and joined Charlie on the footpath.

"You are extremely brave, Annie," said Hank, "but try not to put your life on the line every day, huh? And remember, listen to your brother now and again. He's not that bad!"

Annie replied in a really sleepy voice, "Just call me 'Ace'."

Charlie and Hank exchanged glances, as if to say, she's one of us now, a real detective, bitten by the investigation bug.

Hank drove away and Charlie and Annie were left standing on the street. Charlie felt slightly hurt, having had no idea that Hank was only planning to use him on one case. But there was nothing he could do about it now. May as well just go home.

Hank drove away, turning the radio on in his car and humming along with the music. He felt bad about the kid but felt good about himself! He'd done it! He'd found out from TG who had committed the murder. He hadn't acted on what he'd been told. Instead he'd let Charlie get on with it and the kid had pretty much come up trumps! Success!

The Court of Ghouls would have to quash his sentence now. He could pass peacefully over to the other side, instead of having to spend eternity stuck in Glasgow, limping from one crime scene to another.

CHAPTER ELEVEN
THE VERDICT

HANK was back in the Court Of Ghouls. He'd forgotten just how gruesome they were. TG was by his side, waiting to hear what the judges had to say.

Hank cleared his throat. He wished they would hurry up. The white one was shuffling papers, reading and re-reading the evidence, which had been put in front of him. Finally he spoke.

"So, Mr Kane, how do you think you have performed?"

Hank smiled confidently. "Extremely well," he said. "I did what you asked. I let Charlie solve the case by himself. I didn't help him at all. The boy was brilliant. What more can I say?"

The twins turned towards Hank. "What about all the evidence?" they asked in unison.

"Handed over to the police," answered Hank.

The twins sighed. "Did you *help* with the evidence or did Charlie get it by himself?"

Hank felt himself starting to perspire.

"The kid got it by himself. He went to the

Jackson home one night..." He took his handkerchief from his pocket and wiped the sweat from his upper lip.

The judge whose flesh was having trouble staying on his face spoke next. "Did you plant any evidence, Detective Kane?"

"Well, not exactly, I mean, I..." Hank stammered.

"Where did the rat poison come from? Did the boy find it by himself, or was he helped by you?"

Hank sat down. He hung his head. They knew. They knew he had planted the rat poison. Even though he knew that was the way Emily Jackson had killed her husband, he still wasn't allowed to provide the evidence. How were you supposed to prove a case if you couldn't plant the evidence? That aside, he realised now that he was stupid to think he could have got away with it.

He stood, eyes downcast, realising his sentence was anything but over.

"Please try harder next time, Detective Kane. And remember, we will be watching you," hissed the white one as Hank and TG left the room.

* * * * * *

One night, about a month later, Hank was back in his office in Glasgow. He examined his reflection in the mirror. The skeleton-look definitely wasn't flattering but what was the point in wasting his special compound when he wasn't planning on going out.

His phone rang and he picked it up. He had a short conversation with the caller and replaced the receiver.

He picked up the phone again and dialled a number.

"Kid? Better get down here right away. We're back in business."

OTHER TITLES IN THE DEAD DETECTIVE SERIES:

SIX FEET UNDER

Hank falls and knocks himself out while chasing a thief from his office. He's forgotten to take his "medicine bottle" with him and his flesh starts disappearing, revealing his bony white skeleton underneath. Everybody is talking about the "well-dressed Skeleton" found lying in the street. His old-fashioned 1940s clothes and hat look very strange. The police, after forensic tests, have the body buried. Is this really the end of Hank Cane? It will be, unless Charlie can work out Hank's secret code in the letter in his desk drawer, marked "ONLY TO BE OPENED IN AN EMERGENCY". If this isn't an emergency what is? But can Charlie handle all the secrets in the letter?

DEAD LOSS

Hank gets a visit from the ghost of murder victim Tony Falco, begging for help. Tony, a cat burglar, had stolen jewels on him when he died and the Court of Ghouls won't let Tony into Bandit Heaven until he returns them. Just one problem though – no-one found Falco's body. It's lost! Hank thinks that the Grim Reaper might have some clues. His apprentice, Charlie, is desperate to solve the case without help of any "dead guys", but he disappears! Now the Grim Reaper and Falco have a body full of loot to find – and the apprentice too!

THE CORPSE THAT SANG

A Corpse seen in 1940's Los Angeles turns up in 2002, singing on TV! The strangest coincidence – or is Hank's old flame haunting him. She was a great detective who ended up in Sleuth Heaven – so, why give that up just to sing? Charlie sees the romantic side of Hank and wants to throw up! How can they solve cases with Hank staring at the TV all night? For the first time, Charlie has to take the calls at Hank's office. At last, the Kid can prove his worth, and he resolves to break the case of *The Corpse That Sang*.

THROW AWAY THE KEY

"Help me... please, help me!" A voice identifying itself only as "The Prisoner" keeps calling Hank's phone, pleading for help. Despite being asked why, the panicking voice just keeps calling. Charlie introduces Hank to the latest technology in phone tapping and they listen carefully to the background noises, searching for clues. They get worried when they begin to recognise some sounds, which are too familar for comfort. The Prisoner is very, very close to home!!

GHOST CAR 49

The siren from an old-fashioned American police car is heard echoing around the streets at night. The sound of screeching tyres, blaring police radio, 1940s jazz music and constant gunfire freak out the local residents. Needless to say, Charlie gets the call: " Better get over here, Kid. Looks like we've got something." But how will they bring Car 49 to a halt? And who is at the wheel?!

THE DEAD DETECTIVE SERIES

Dead and Unburied	1-904684-00-9
Six Feet Under	1-904684-01-7
Dead Loss	1-904684-02-5
Throw Away The Key	1-904684-04-1
The Corpse That Sang	1-904684-03-3
Ghost Car 49	1-904684-05-X

www.booksnoir.com

Hey guys! Hank Kane here. Check out my website www.deaddetective.com *to keep up to date with my interactive e-book* Web of Intrigue, *an internet adventure where you, the reader, can help me on the case.*

P.S. You'd better be good!